Don't Judge
by what
You See

Ashira Greenberg

Illustrated by Racheli Edelstein

ISRAEL BOOKSHOP
PUBLICATIONS

Illustrated by: Racheli Edelstein
Book design by: Rivkah Lewis

Distributed by:
Israel Bookshop Publications
501 Prospect Street
Lakewood, NJ 08701

Tel: (732) 901-3009
Fax: (732) 901-4012
www.israelbookshoppublications.com
info@israelbookshoppublications.com

Printed in the United States of America

Distributed in Israel by:
Shanky's
Petach Tikva 16
Jerusalem
972-2-538-6936

Distributed in Europe by:
Lehmanns
Unit E Viking Industrial Park
Rolling Mill Road,
Jarrow , Tyne & Wear NE32 3DP
44-191-406-0842

Distributed in Australia by:
Gold's Book and Gift Company
3- 13 William Street
Balaclava 3183
613-9527-8775

Distributed in South Africa by:
Kollel Bookshop
Ivy Common
107 William Road, Norwood
Johannesburg 2192
27-11-728-1822

THIS BOOK IS DEDICATED TO my family, friends from Camp Simcha and Kids of Courage, friends from school and around the neighborhood, elementary and junior high school teachers, doctors, therapists, shadows and everyone else who has helped me over the years, with tremendous appreciation for your caring support and friendship.

Special thanks to Israel Bookshop Publications for helping to make my dream of publishing a book a reality.

ASHIRA GREENBERG is a seventeen-year-old girl who has cerebral palsy and attends a mainstream yeshiva high school in the greater New York area. When Ashira is not busy with her schoolwork or therapies, she enjoys writing, listening to music and being with friends. Ashira has been involved in Camp Simcha Special and Kids of Courage for the past few years, and her friends from these places were a great inspiration and resource for writing this book.

One Sunday morning, just as I was planning my day,
My friend Malky called; she needed help right away.
She was making a party that afternoon,
But had forgotten about dessert, and her guests were coming soon!

I told Malky I would love to help, and I asked her what to do.
She asked if I would please bake a cake and decorate it, too.
"Sure!" I said. "I even have a cookbook right here."
"Thanks, and call if you need help," said Malky, her voice filled with cheer.

My cookbook had so many recipes; I picked one that did not look long.
I wanted to make the cake quickly, without anything going wrong.
In my rush, however, things did not go right.
I confused the salt with the sugar, because both of them are white!

Quickly I called Malky and asked, "What should I do?"
"You need to start over," she said, "and pay more attention to cake number two!

Although salt and sugar look alike, they do not taste the same;
When dealing with ingredients, you must look at each container's name.

**"We cannot judge something just by what we see—
Sometimes things are different than we expect them to be."**

So off to start a new cake I ran.
I looked the recipe over carefully, and again I began.
The new batter was doing well, and I was very excited.
My cake would be great, and Malky would be delighted.

But when I got to the vanilla, I felt myself frown.
The vanilla I knew was white, but now I saw brown!
I thought to myself, *This simply cannot be right.*
Something must be wrong; vanilla is supposed to be white.

Back to the phone I raced: "Malky, the vanilla is brown; do you know why?"
"Baking vanilla is always brown!" was Malky's instant reply.

> **"We cannot judge something
> just by what we see—
> Sometimes things are different
> than we expect them to be."**

So I continued measuring and mixing, then poured the batter into a pan.
Into the oven it went, and the baking process began.

The timer rang after an hour; my cake was finally done.
I took out the frosting and sprinkles and started to have some fun!
Just then I heard a small voice: "Can I please help you?"
It was my three-year-old brother; he wanted to have fun, too.

"After I frost the cake, you can put sprinkles in this place,"
I said, pointing to a spot, and a smile covered his little face.

I should have known my little brother would make a mistake.
He took the sprinkles and spilled them *all over* the cake!

There was no time to fix it; I was already late.
Malky needed my cake; how could I make her wait?
So I took it as it was, and hurried out the door,
Never dreaming there would be more surprises in store!

When I reached Malky's house, I heard music playing in the backyard.
I followed the sound of the music, but finding my friend was hard.
The backyard was filled with girls whom I did not expect to meet;
Many of them had problems with their hands or with their feet.

Some could walk, while others needed to sit in a wheelchair.
Then there were those who had to use a machine to get air.
Some girls had special tubes to help them get food.
I tried not to stare at them, because that would be rude.

Still, seeing these guests was really a sight;
They looked funny; none of their bodies looked right.
Then I thought, *If I stare, they probably won't even know.*
Their bodies are not right; maybe their minds are also slow.

13

So I stood near the group staring, not knowing what to say.
Finally, one of the girls came over to me and asked if I was okay.
"Yes," I answered in an extra-sweet voice, "thank you."
The girl then asked me, "Do you want to join us, too?"

I agreed to join them, and to my great surprise,
There was a lot more to them than what met my eyes.
They were talking and laughing; some were playing a game,
They acted just like my friends, even if their bodies weren't the same.

I realized that these girls knew I had been staring;
They knew that my extra-sweet voice did not reflect caring.
There was nothing wrong with their minds; I'd made a big mistake.
One more slip-up for the day, I thought, remembering the cake.

As I walked around some more, I was stopped by another guest.
She approached me with what I thought was a strange request.
"Would you get me some water to take with my medicine?"
"Sure," I responded, though with an unsure grin.

I whispered to the girl, "Is everything okay?"
"Of course," the girl said. "I take medicine *every day*."
Now I was confused; the girl looked and sounded quite well;
Why she would need medicine, I simply couldn't tell.

Suddenly I spotted Malky, and, my curiosity getting stronger,
I ran to her with my questions, unable to keep them in any longer.
I asked how the girls who look different could still be happy as can be.
And what could be wrong with someone who looks healthy to me?

"When we see someone," Malky told me, "we cannot judge her by sight."
"Just like sugar and salt," I said. "Both of them are white!"
"Exactly!" replied Malky. "Just by looking you cannot tell,
Which person is sick and which person is well.

**"We cannot judge something
just by what we see—
Sometimes things are different
than we expect them to be."**

I told Malky about the girls I had been with just before.
"They are like the baking vanilla," she said, and didn't need to say more.
Just like the vanilla, whose color makes it seem like something is wrong,
The girls who looked very different were actually able and strong.

19

Malky had prepared a table especially for my cake.
I was embarrassed, though, because of the sprinkle mistake.
Malky told me the cake was fine; she had not asked for a fancy treat;
All she really wanted was a dessert tasty and sweet.

"You don't have to worry about the ruined design;
The outside doesn't count, as long as the inside—the taste—is fine.

"Remember, we cannot judge something
just by what we see—
It can really be different
than how the outside appears to be."

I was happy to hear that, but then I thought of something new.
"Malky," I said, "I have a question to ask you.
If there are guests who are unable to cut a piece of cake,
Then how exactly are they going to manage to take?"

"I know!" Malky said. "You and I will cut the whole cake.
Whoever wants a piece can just come and take.
No one will feel bad for not cutting a piece alone;
We will not even know who can and cannot cut cake on their own."

Malky and I smiled at each other as we cut the cake and gave it away.
I couldn't believe how many lessons I had learned on that day!

We cannot judge anyone just by what we see—
Sometimes situations are different than we'd expect them to be.
We must give all a chance to be who they truly are,
Because under the wrappings, you might find a real star!